Revolting Arithmetic: Invaders

Rowland Morgan

Revolting Arithmetic: Invaders

The invaders came...

... and some of them liked it so much, they stayed!

Editor: Terry Vittachi
Illustrations: Andrew Noble – Andrew Noble Design Team Ltd
                   Gary Clifford – The Drawing Room
Layout artist: Jane Conway
Cover image: Gary Clifford – The Drawing Room
Cover design: Ed Gallagher

© 2000 Belair Publications, on behalf of the author.

Every effort has been made to contact copyright holders of material used in this book. If any have been overlooked, we will be pleased to make any necessary arrangements.

First published 2000 by Belair Publications, Dunstable.

Belair Publications, Albert House, Apex Business Centre, Boscombe Road, Dunstable, LU5 4RL, England.

ISBN 1–84191–036–8

Printed in Singapore by Craft Print Pte Ltd.

Contents

Fierce Fighters

When the invaders landed, the natives were ready!

Introduction

Cross-curricular maths

Most people agree that there is a maths problem in Britain. Pupils tend not to like it much, teachers are in short supply and results could be better. Maths is not as popular as it could be. Sadly, that has been taken for granted.

Why has maths got a bad name when, of all the subjects in primary school, maths is the one where there is often a definite right answer or a wrong one? It is the subject in which you can learn an operation, perform it and get marks. It is quite straightforward.

People use maths all the time. In a game of darts, working out a knitting pattern, checking bank accounts – there are so many ways people enjoy their command of numbers, without thinking about it.

Revolting Arithmetic takes a shot at motivating children's enjoyment of maths by integrating parts of it with history. Children will just say: cross-curricular, here we come!

How to use this book

These activities are intended to help children practise their mathematics in the context of work on historical topics. They could be used for homework or for additional mathematical work outside the daily maths lesson. You may want children to write directly on the sheets, or they may be used as resource material, with pupils recording their answers elsewhere.

To give the flexibility to match the activities to work in different year groups or to children of differing ability, the copiable activity pages are laid out in three gradations of difficulty.

Level 1 uses mathematical operations (mostly arithmetic) at a level roughly equivalent to Year 3. This should suit most children in Years 3–4. Level 2 is more appropriate to Years 4–5. Level 3 is aimed at Years 5–6.

There is a self-checking function on each sheet in which we sometimes push the agenda a little, in the hope that self-marking will motivate some stretching. You may want some children to use a calculator for this. Answers and algorithms are provided at the back of the book.

Early Britain

Is there a wilder and woollier patch of history than the days of the Viking pirates? Their longship exploits remain a wonder of the world, however gory and barbaric. Equally dramatic was the evangelisation of the British invaders, and the fierce adoption by pagans of one true god. For centuries, peoples fought for supremacy across

the island, culminating in the most famous battle of them all in 1066. Centuries earlier, the British held out against the invading Angles, perhaps led by a charismatic king called Arthur. However, his romantic story is just that, romance. He and his round table are missing from the historical record – and so from this book.

British Battles

1 The Roman emperor Claudius ordered the invasion of Britain in AD43. The last time the Romans had invaded Britain was in 54BC. How many years were there between the two invasions?
(Remember: BC dates go down, AD dates go up!)

2 The Roman governor flogged Boudicca, queen of one of the Celtic tribes of Britain. Furious, she gathered an army and attacked Londinium (London) in AD61. How many years had it been since Claudius invaded?

3 When Boudicca's army attacked, the Roman governor was away. He rushed back to London. In two days, he had got half-way. At this rate, how many days would the whole journey take?

4 When the Roman army finally faced the Celtic army, the Celtic women fought beside their husbands. They were all killed with the Celtic army. If each Celtic soldier had a wife, what fraction of the Celtic army was women?

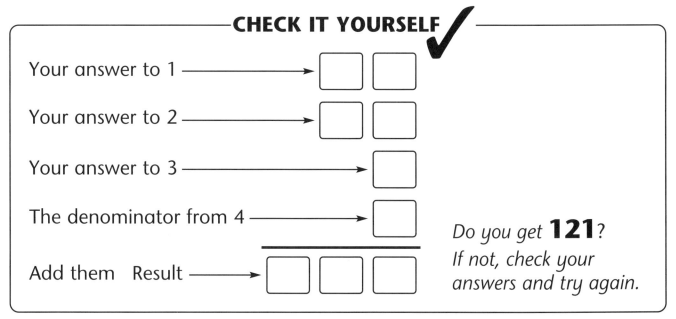

CHECK IT YOURSELF ✔

Your answer to 1 ⟶ ☐ ☐

Your answer to 2 ⟶ ☐ ☐

Your answer to 3 ⟶ ☐

The denominator from 4 ⟶ ☐

Add them   Result ⟶ ☐ ☐ ☐

*Do you get **121**?
If not, check your answers and try again.*

British Battles

1   The Roman emperor Claudius ordered the invasion of Britain in AD43. The last time Britain had been invaded was in 54BC, by Julius Caesar. In round numbers, how many centuries divided the two invasions? (Remember: BC dates go down, AD dates go up!)

2   The Roman governor flogged Boudicca, queen of one of the Celtic tribes of Britain. Enraged, she gathered an army and attacked Londinium (London) in AD61. Her army killed 60 000 Romans. If one Celtic soldier killed 75 Romans a day for nine days, how many Romans would he kill?

3   When Boudicca's army revolted, the Roman governor was busy killing Druids in Anglesey. He rushed back to Londinium, a three-day march. If he started out with one legion and eight more joined him each day, how many did he have when he arrived in Londinium?

4   When the Roman army finally faced the Celtic army, the Celtic women fought beside their husbands. They were all killed with the Celtic army. If one in every two Celtic soldiers had a wife, what fraction of the Celtic army in its final battle was women?

CHECK IT YOURSELF ✔

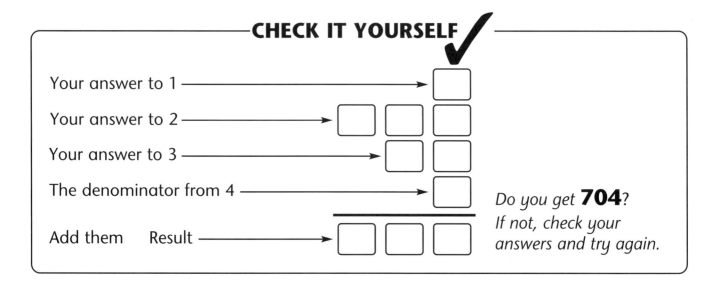

Your answer to 1 ⟶ ☐

Your answer to 2 ⟶ ☐ ☐ ☐

Your answer to 3 ⟶ ☐ ☐

The denominator from 4 ⟶ ☐

Add them   Result ⟶ ☐ ☐ ☐

Do you get **704**?
If not, check your answers and try again.

British Battles

1 The Roman emperor Claudius ordered the invasion of Britain, 97 years after it had last been invaded by Julius Caesar in 54BC. In what year did Claudius order the invasion? (Remember: BC dates go down, AD dates go up!)

2 The Roman governor flogged Boudicca, queen of one of the Celtic tribes of Britain. Enraged, she gathered an army and attacked Londinium (London) in AD61. Her army killed a total of 60 000 Romans. If 42 867 of them were killed in Londinium, how many were killed in attacks on other Roman towns?

3 When Boudicca's army revolted, the Roman governor was busy killing Druids in Anglesey. He rushed back to Londinium, a three-day march. If he started out with 12 500 soldiers and 950 more joined him each day, how many did he have when he arrived in Londinium?

4 When the Roman army finally faced the Celtic army, the Celtic women fought beside their husbands. They were all killed with the Celtic army. If one in every two Celtic soldiers had a wife and 25 000 women were killed, how many men were in the Celtic army?

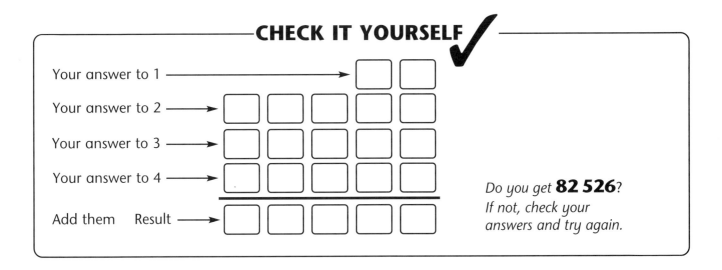

CHECK IT YOURSELF ✔

Your answer to 1 ⟶ ☐ ☐

Your answer to 2 ⟶ ☐ ☐ ☐ ☐ ☐

Your answer to 3 ⟶ ☐ ☐ ☐ ☐ ☐

Your answer to 4 ⟶ ☐ ☐ ☐ ☐ ☐

Add them   Result ⟶ ☐ ☐ ☐ ☐ ☐

*Do you get **82 526**? If not, check your answers and try again.*

Revolting Arithmetic: *Invaders*

Roman Roads

1 You are a Roman soldier. You have to find your way around Britain using this map. How many main roads are there?

2 How many kilometres is it from Cirencester to Leicester?

3 How long is the Fosse Way altogether?

4 How many kilometres is it from Lincoln to Wroxeter?

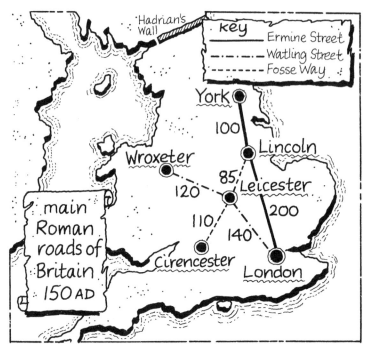

key
— Ermine Street
—·— Watling Street
--- Fosse Way

Hadrian's Wall

York 100 Lincoln
Wroxeter 120 85 Leicester 200
110 140
Cirencester London

main Roman roads of Britain 150 AD

5 How many kilometres is it from Lincoln to Leicester and back again?

CHECK IT YOURSELF ✔

Your answer to 1 ⟶ ☐

Your answer to 2 ⟶ **1** ☐ ☐

Your answer to 3 ⟶ **1** ☐ ☐

Your answer to 4 ⟶ **2** ☐ ☐

Your answer to 5 ⟶ **1** ☐ ☐

Add them   Result ⟶ **6** ☐ ☐

*Do you get **683**? If not, check your answers and try again.*

Roman Roads

1   You are a Roman soldier. You have to find your way around Britain using this map. You have to march from Wroxeter to York, using the main road. How many kilometres is that?

2   How many kilometres is it from London to Wroxeter?

3   How many kilometres is it from Lincoln to Cirencester and back again, along the Fosse Way?

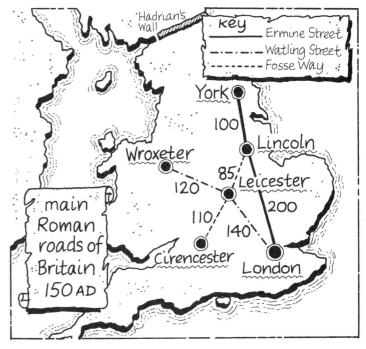

4   How many kilometres would you have to march to reach London from York, visiting Leicester on the way?

5   You reach Leicester. A message from your centurion calls you back to Wroxeter. The message says the journey will take three days. How many kilometres does the centurion intend you to walk each day?

CHECK IT YOURSELF ✓

Your answer to 1 ⟶ ☐ ☐ ☐

Your answer to 2 ⟶ ☐ ☐ ☐

Your answer to 3 ⟶ ☐ ☐ ☐

Your answer to 4 ⟶ ☐ ☐ ☐

Your answer to 5 ⟶ ☐ ☐

Add them   Result ⟶ ☐ ☐ ☐ ☐

Do you get **1320**? *If not, check your answers and try again.*

Roman Roads

3

1 You are a Roman soldier posted to Britain. Using this map, you try to work out how far you might have to march while you are here. How many kilometres long are Ermine Street, Watling Street and Fosse Way, added together?

2 Your centurion says you will be marching from London to Leicester, Leicester to Lincoln, then on to York. Coming back, you will take a short cut going from York to Lincoln, then straight on to London. How many kilometres is that altogether?

3 Watling Street runs from London to Wroxeter via Leicester. Your centurion orders you to march along it, then changes his mind exactly half-way. How far are you from Leicester?

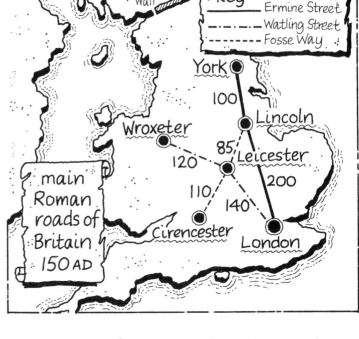

key
— Ermine Street
-·-·- Watling Street
---- Fosse Way

York ●
100
Lincoln ●
Wroxeter ●
120   85   Leicester ●
110   200
140
Cirencester ●   London ●

main Roman roads of Britain 150 AD

4 Your legion is very fit and can march from Leicester to London at ten kilometres an hour without a break. How many hours does the journey take you?

5 You have some heavy weapons to carry and can only march at eight kilometres an hour. How many hours will it take you to get from London to Cirencester via Leicester? (Round your answer to the nearest whole number.)

CHECK IT YOURSELF ✔

Your answer to 1 ⟶ ☐ ☐ ☐

Your answer to 2 ⟶ ☐ ☐ ☐

Your answer to 3 ⟶ ☐ ☐

Your answer to 4 ⟶ ☐ ☐

Fill in the whole number from 5 ⟶ ☐ ☐

Add them   Result ⟶ ☐ ☐ ☐ ☐

Do you get **1435**?
If not, check your answers and try again.

Slave Statistics

1 In seventy-three BC a slave called Spartacus led a slaves' revolt. Write that year in figures.

2 In 132BC there had been another revolt. How many years were there between that earlier revolt and the revolt led by Spartacus? (Remember, BC dates go down, not up.)

3 Romans encouraged their slaves to have children, because they could be extra servants. If five slave couples each had eight children, how many extra servants would the master have?

4 Masters had the power to set their slaves free. If one master had 12 slaves and set half of them free, how many slaves would he have left?

SILVIUS THE SOLDIER SAYS
The Roman Empire was based on slavery. Roman citizens were free. Their servants were slaves. Most farm labour was done by slaves. As the Empire grew, so did the number of slaves.

CHECK IT YOURSELF ✔

Your answer to 1 ⟶ ☐ ☐

Your answer to 2 ⟶ ☐ ☐

Your answer to 3 ⟶ ☐ ☐

Your answer to 4 ⟶ ☐

Add them   Result ⟶ ☐ ☐ ☐

Do you get **178**?
If not, check your answers and try again.

Slave Statistics

1 In 73BC a gladiator slave called Spartacus led a slaves' revolt. He formed an army of sixty thousand slaves. Write that number in figures.

2 In another slaves' revolt in 132BC, 20 000 slaves were crucified. Others were worked to death rowing warships. If 21 slaves in a house revolted and one-third of them were crucified, how many would remain?

3 Romans encouraged their slaves to have children, because they could be extra servants or they could be sold. If 15 slave couples working on a farm each had eight children, how many extra servants would the master have?

4 Masters had the power to set their slaves free, turning them into Roman citizens. If one master had 15 slaves and set one-fifth of them free, how many slaves would he have left?

SILVIUS THE SOLDIER SAYS
The Roman Empire was based on slavery. Roman citizens were free. Their servants were slaves. Most farm labour was done by slaves. As the Empire grew, so did the number of slaves.

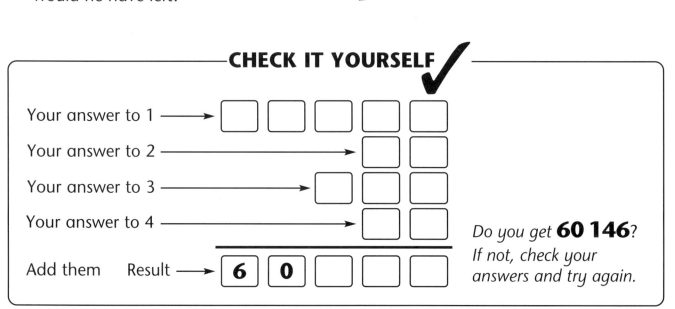

CHECK IT YOURSELF ✔

Your answer to 1 ⟶ ☐ ☐ ☐ ☐ ☐

Your answer to 2 ⟶ ☐ ☐

Your answer to 3 ⟶ ☐ ☐ ☐

Your answer to 4 ⟶ ☐ ☐

Add them   Result ⟶ **6** **0** ☐ ☐ ☐

Do you get **60 146**? *If not, check your answers and try again.*

Slave Statistics

1 In 73BC a gladiator slave called Spartacus led a slaves' revolt. He formed an army of 42 550 slaves. Soon, another 17 450 joined him. How big was his army?

2 In 132BC there had been another slaves' revolt. It was crushed and 20 000 slaves were crucified. If one-quarter of the slaves were crucified, how many actually revolted?

SILVIUS THE SOLDIER SAYS
The Roman Empire was based on slavery. Roman citizens were free. Their servants were slaves. Most farm labour was done by slaves. As the Empire grew, so did the number of slaves.

3 Romans encouraged their slaves to have children, because they could be added to the staff as extra servants, or sold. If nine slave couples working for one master had an average of 8.4 children each, how many extra servants would the master have (to the nearest one)?

4 Masters had the power to set their slaves free, turning them into Roman citizens. If one master had 12 slaves and set 75 per cent of them free, how many slaves would he have left?

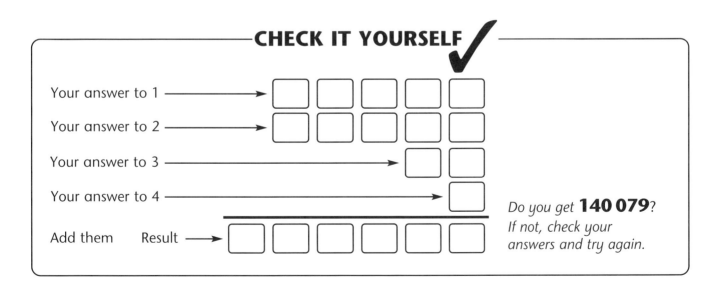

CHECK IT YOURSELF ✔

Your answer to 1 ⟶ ☐ ☐ ☐ ☐ ☐

Your answer to 2 ⟶ ☐ ☐ ☐ ☐ ☐

Your answer to 3 ⟶ ☐ ☐

Your answer to 4 ⟶ ☐

Add them   Result ⟶ ☐ ☐ ☐ ☐ ☐ ☐

*Do you get **140 079**? If not, check your answers and try again.*

Ghastly Gladiators

SILVIUS THE SOLDIER SAYS
Gladiators fought one another in arenas to entertain bloodthirsty crowds!

1 Fighting like this began in ancient Greece two hundred and fifty years before. Write that number in figures.

2 There were many types of gladiator such as:
   a) the retiarius, who fought with a trident and net;
   b) a murmillo, who had a sword, shield and helmet; and
   c) a thracian, who had a dagger and shield.
   How many pieces of equipment do the gladiators have between them?

3 If 121 gladiators begged for mercy and 36 of them were killed, how many lived to fight again?

4 If eight pairs were fighting, how many gladiators were there altogether?

CHECK IT YOURSELF ✔

Your answer to 1 ⟶ ☐ ☐ ☐

Your answer to 2 ⟶ ☐

Your answer to 3 ⟶ ☐ ☐

Your answer to 4 ⟶ ☐ ☐

Add them   Result ⟶ **3** ☐ ☐

*Do you get **358**? If not, check your answers and try again.*

Ghastly Gladiators

SILVIUS THE SOLDIER SAYS
"We who are about to die salute you!" That was the gladiators' cry as they paraded in a Roman arena. It was their dreadful job to murder or to be murdered, in front of a cheering crowd.

1 Fighting like this began in ancient Greece. Two hundred and fifty years later, it was bloodthirsty entertainment for the Romans. More than ten thousand gladiators died in the ring. Write that number in figures.

3 A wounded gladiator could beg the crowd for mercy. If the crowd showed thumbs up, he lived. If they showed thumbs down, the other gladiator had to murder him. If 245 gladiators begged for mercy and 186 of them got the thumbs down, how many lived to fight again?

2 There were many types of gladiator, including:
   a) the retiarius, who fought with a trident and net;
   b) a murmillo, who had a sword, shield and helmet; and
   c) a thracian, who had a dagger and shield.
Count the pieces of equipment they have between them. If five of each kind of gladiator fought together, how many pieces of equipment were needed?

4 In a large arena, several pairs of gladiators fought at the same time. If 14 pairs were fighting, how many gladiators were there altogether?

CHECK IT YOURSELF ✔

Your answer to 1 → ☐ ☐ ☐ ☐ ☐

Your answer to 2 → ☐ ☐

Your answer to 3 → ☐ ☐

Your answer to 4 → ☐ ☐

Add them   Result → **1** **0** ☐ ☐ ☐

Do you get **10 122**? *If not, check your answers and try again.*

Ghastly Gladiators

SILVIUS THE SOLDIER SAYS
"We who are about to die salute you!" That was the gladiators' cry as they paraded in a Roman arena. They were unfortunate men, usually slaves, prisoners or criminals. It was their dreadful job to murder or be murdered, in front of a cheering crowd.

1 Fighting like this began in ancient Greece. Two hundred and fifty years later, it was bloodthirsty entertainment for the Romans. If it cost $2\frac{1}{2}$ pieces of silver to watch the games for half a day, how many pieces of silver did it cost a family of four to watch three whole days of games?

3 A wounded gladiator could beg for mercy. If the crowd showed thumbs up, he lived. If they showed thumbs down, he died. If 2440 gladiators begged for mercy during the year, and 25 per cent of them got the thumbs down, how many lived?

2 There were many types of gladiator including:
a) the retiarius, who fought with a trident and net;
b) a murmillo, who had a sword, shield and helmet; and
c) a thracian, who had a dagger and shield.
If 32 of each kind of gladiator fight together, how many pieces of equipment will they need?

4 In a large arena, several pairs of gladiators fought at the same time. If 54 pairs of gladiators were fighting and one in three were killed, how many gladiators lived to fight again?

CHECK IT YOURSELF ✔

Your answer to 1 ⟶ ☐ ☐

Your answer to 2 ⟶ ☐ ☐ ☐

Your answer to 3 ⟶ ☐ ☐ ☐ ☐

Your answer to 4 ⟶ ☐ ☐

Add them   Result ⟶ ☐ ☐ ☐ ☐

*Do you get **2186**?*
If not, check your answers and try again.

Kingdoms & Counties

1 Anglo-Saxon kings had councils called witans. The witan gave land to knights, who were called thanes. The thanes had to supply soldiers to the king. Suppose the circled numbers are the numbers of thanes in each kingdom. How many thanes are there in Wessex?

2 How many thanes are there in Mercia and Northumbria?

3 If East Anglia, Essex, Kent and Sussex joined together, how many thanes would they have?

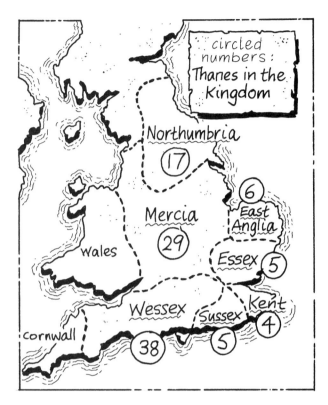

circled numbers: Thanes in the Kingdom

Northumbria ⑰

Mercia ㉙

Wales

East Anglia ⑥

Essex ⑤

Wessex ㊳

Sussex ⑤

Kent ④

Cornwall

4 Suppose Essex attacked Wessex and Mercia and killed 14 of their thanes. How many thanes would be left in Wessex and Mercia?

CHECK IT YOURSELF ✔

Your answer to 1 ⟶ ☐ ☐

Your answer to 2 ⟶ ☐ ☐

Your answer to 3 ⟶ ☐ ☐

Your answer to 4 ⟶ ☐ ☐

Add them   Result ⟶ ☐ ☐ ☐

Do you get **157**? *If not, check your answers and try again.*

Revolting Arithmetic: *Invaders*

Kingdoms & Counties

1 A king from the royal family ruled each Anglo-Saxon kingdom. The king had a council called a witan. The witan gave land to knights, who in return had to supply soldiers to the king. The knights were called thanes. Suppose the circled numbers are the numbers of thanes in each kingdom. How many thanes are there in Anglo-Saxon Britain?

2 If the thanes of Mercia and Northumbria trained nine archers each, how many archers would they have?

3 If East Anglia, Essex, Kent and Sussex formed an alliance and their thanes trained seven swordsmen each, how many swordsmen would they have?

4 Suppose the thanes of Wessex and Mercia trained eight cavalrymen each; how many cavalrymen would they have?

CHECK IT YOURSELF ✔

Your answer to 1 ⟶ ☐ ☐ ☐

Your answer to 2 ⟶ ☐ ☐ ☐

Your answer to 3 ⟶ ☐ ☐ ☐

Your answer to 4 ⟶ ☐ ☐ ☐

Add them   Result ⟶ ☐ ☐ ☐ ☐

Do you get **1194**? *If not, check your answers and try again.*

Kingdoms & Counties

1 A king from the royal family ruled each Anglo-Saxon kingdom. The king had a council called a witan. The witan gave land to knights, who in return had to supply soldiers to the king. The knights were called thanes. Suppose the circled numbers are the numbers of thanes in each kingdom. Each thane trains nine archers. How many archers do the thanes of Anglo-Saxon Britain supply?

2 If the thanes of Mercia and Northumbria trained 36 battle-axe warriors each, how many battle-axe warriors would they have?

3 If East Anglia, Essex, Kent and Sussex formed an alliance and their thanes trained 55 swordsmen each, how many swordsmen would they have?

4 Suppose the thanes of Wessex and Mercia trained 28 mounted knights each. How many mounted knights would they have?

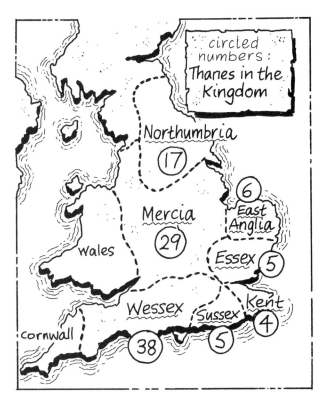

CHECK IT YOURSELF ✔

Your answer to 1 ⟶ ☐ ☐ ☐

Your answer to 2 ⟶ ☐ ☐ ☐ ☐

Your answer to 3 ⟶ ☐ ☐ ☐ ☐

Your answer to 4 ⟶ ☐ ☐ ☐ ☐

Add them   Result ⟶ ☐ ☐ ☐ ☐

*Do you get **5568**? If not, check your answers and try again.*

Farming Figures

1 Egbert is a Viking sailor who has settled in Northumbria. His father has helped him buy one hundred and forty-two animals. Write that number in figures.

2 Egbert has 58 chickens and 33 ducks. How many birds does he have?

3 The birds give three dozen eggs a month altogether. How many eggs is that?

4 Egbert has 15 cows, a bull and 12 calves. How many cattle is that?

5 Egbert has five sows, one boar and 18 piglets. How many pigs is that?

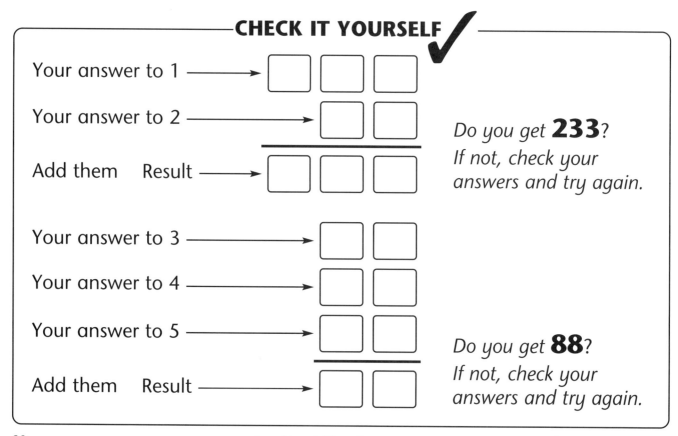

CHECK IT YOURSELF ✔

Your answer to 1 ⟶ ☐ ☐ ☐

Your answer to 2 ⟶ ☐ ☐

Add them   Result ⟶ ☐ ☐ ☐

Do you get **233**? *If not, check your answers and try again.*

Your answer to 3 ⟶ ☐ ☐

Your answer to 4 ⟶ ☐ ☐

Your answer to 5 ⟶ ☐ ☐

Add them   Result ⟶ ☐ ☐

Do you get **88**? *If not, check your answers and try again.*

Revolting Arithmetic: *Invaders*

Farming Figures

1 Egbert is a Viking sailor who has settled in Northumbria to raise a family. His farmhouse is built of stone, with a thatched roof. His father has helped him buy animals. Egbert has 72 poultry birds. Half of them are chickens. How many chickens does he have?

2 The poultry give nine dozen eggs a month in total. How many eggs is that?

3 Egbert has 15 cows and a bull. One third of the cows have had five calves each. The rest have had six. How many calves have they had altogether?

4 Egbert has five sows and one boar. Each sow has had 12 piglets and half of them have been eaten by Egbert and his family. How many are left?

CHECK IT YOURSELF ✓

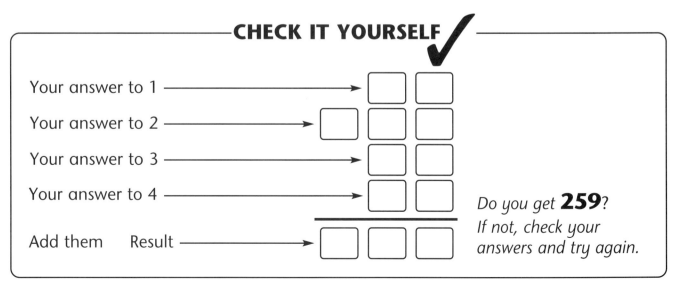

Your answer to 1 ⟶ ☐ ☐

Your answer to 2 ⟶ ☐ ☐ ☐

Your answer to 3 ⟶ ☐ ☐

Your answer to 4 ⟶ ☐ ☐

Add them   Result ⟶ ☐ ☐ ☐

Do you get **259**? *If not, check your answers and try again.*

Farming Figures

1 Egbert is a Viking sailor who has settled in Northumbria to raise a family. His house is built of stone, with a thatched roof. Like the other 14 farmers in the valley, Egbert has 72 chickens. How many chickens do they have between them?

2 His poultry give nine dozen eggs a month. How many is that per year?

3 Egbert has 16 cows and a bull. Twenty-five per cent of the cows have had five calves each. Seventy-five per cent have had three. How many calves does Egbert have?

4 Egbert has 14 sows and one boar. Each sow has had 12 piglets and half of them have been eaten by Egbert and his family or taken to market. How many are left?

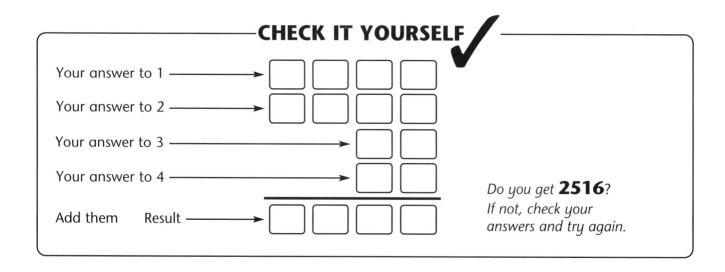

CHECK IT YOURSELF ✓

Your answer to 1 ⟶ ☐ ☐ ☐ ☐

Your answer to 2 ⟶ ☐ ☐ ☐ ☐

Your answer to 3 ⟶ ☐ ☐

Your answer to 4 ⟶ ☐ ☐

Add them   Result ⟶ ☐ ☐ ☐ ☐

Do you get **2516**? *If not, check your answers and try again.*

Nave, Tower & Transept  1

1 Anglo-Saxons had built a Christian church in every town and village by about AD six hundred and fifty. Write that year in figures.

2 Here is a plan of a church. Use the key to show which end the altar is.

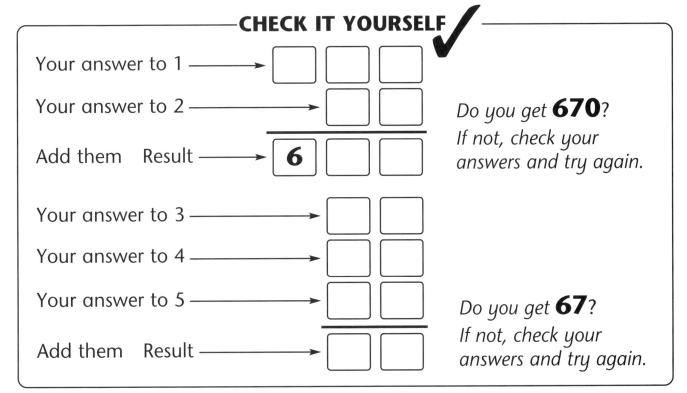

Anglo-Saxon Church-floor plan

Key
North – 10
East – 20
South – 30
West – 40

tower

font
nave
altar

N

5m

5m

12m

8m

3 Use the key to show which end the tower is.

4 Use the key to show on which side of the church the font is.

5 How many metres long is the church?

CHECK IT YOURSELF ✓

Your answer to 1 ⟶ ☐ ☐ ☐

Your answer to 2 ⟶ ☐ ☐

Add them   Result ⟶ **6** ☐ ☐

Do you get **670**? *If not, check your answers and try again.*

Your answer to 3 ⟶ ☐ ☐

Your answer to 4 ⟶ ☐ ☐

Your answer to 5 ⟶ ☐ ☐

Add them   Result ⟶ ☐ ☐

Do you get **67**? *If not, check your answers and try again.*

Revolting Arithmetic: *Invaders*

Nave, Tower & Transept  2

1 By about AD650, Anglo-Saxons had built a Christian church in every town and village. Then, as now, a church was always built facing the same direction. If you stand in the nave facing the altar, through how many degrees will you have to turn to face north?

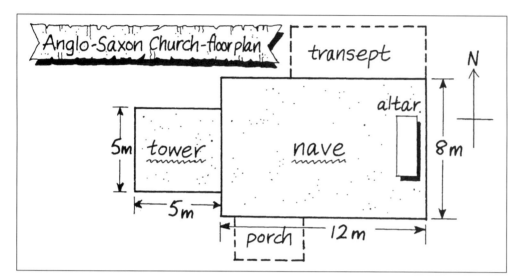

Anglo-Saxon Church-floor plan

transept

N

altar

5m tower

nave

8m

5m

porch 12 m

2 How many square metres is the nave?

3 How many square metres is the floor of the whole church (nave and tower)?

4 A porch of 12 square metres and a transept of 24 square metres are added. How many square metres is the church now?

5 The thatched roof burns. Nine new wooden beams running the length of the nave are needed. How many metres of beam are required?

CHECK IT YOURSELF ✔

Your answer to 1 ⟶ ☐ ☐

Your answer to 2 ⟶ ☐ ☐

Your answer to 3 ⟶ ☐ ☐ ☐

Your answer to 4 ⟶ ☐ ☐ ☐

Your answer to 5 ⟶ ☐ ☐ ☐

Add them   Result ⟶ ☐ ☐ ☐

Do you get **572**? *If not, check your answers and try again.*

Nave, Tower & Transept  3

1 By about AD650 Anglo-Saxons had built a Christian church in every town and village. Then, as now, a church was always built along the same axis. If you stand in the nave facing the tower, through how many degrees must you turn to face the altar?

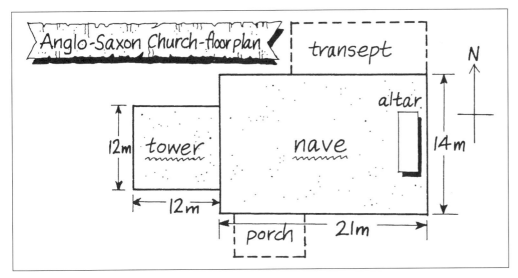

Anglo-Saxon Church-floor plan

transept

tower

nave

altar

12m

12m

porch

21m

14m

N

2 How many square metres is the nave?

3 How many square metres is the floor of the whole church (nave and tower)?

4 A porch and a transept increase the area of the whole church by ten per cent. How many square metres is the church now?

5 The thatched roof burns. Eleven new wooden beams running the length of the nave are needed. How many metres of beam are required?

CHECK IT YOURSELF ✔

Your answer to 1 ⟶ ☐ ☐ ☐ . **0**

Your answer to 2 ⟶ ☐ ☐ ☐ . **0**

Your answer to 3 ⟶ ☐ ☐ ☐ . **0**

Your answer to 4 ⟶ ☐ ☐ ☐ . ☐

Your answer to 5 ⟶ ☐ ☐ ☐ . **0**

Add them   Result ⟶ ☐ ☐ ☐ ☐ . ☐

Do you get **1624.8**? *If not, check your answers and try again.*

Fierce Fighters

1 Poor soldiers, like Harold, could only afford a spear and a simple shield. Richer soldiers, like Alfred, could afford a decorated shield, spear, cloak, brooch and metal helmet. How many pieces of equipment do they have between them?

2 If Danish invaders killed nine poor soldiers like Harold, how many pieces of equipment could they take from them?

3 If the Normans killed eight rich soldiers like Alfred, how many pieces of equipment could they take from them?

4 If 135 poor soldiers and 28 rich soldiers threw their spears at the enemy, how many spears would fly through the air?

Harold and Alfred

5 If 345 soldiers ran into battle and 28 were killed instantly, how many would be left?

CHECK IT YOURSELF ✔

Your answer to 1 ⟶ ☐

Your answer to 2 ⟶ ☐ ☐

Your answer to 5 ⟶ ☐ ☐ ☐

Add them   Result ⟶ **3** ☐ ☐

Do you get **342**? *If not, check your answers and try again.*

Your answer to 3 ⟶ ☐ ☐

Your answer to 4 ⟶ ☐ ☐ ☐

Add them   Result ⟶ ☐ ☐ ☐

Do you get **203**? *If not, check your answers and try again.*

Revolting Arithmetic: *Invaders*

Fierce Fighters

1 Anglo-Saxon soldiers had to provide their own equipment. Poor men, like Harold, could only afford two pieces of equipment: a spear and a simple shield. Richer men, like Alfred, could afford five pieces of equipment: a decorated shield, cloak, brooch, spear and metal helmet. If each piece of equipment cost one piece of silver, how many pieces of silver did it cost to equip a squad of eight poor soldiers and two rich soldiers?

2 If the Danish invaders killed 37 poor soldiers, how many pieces of equipment could they take from them?

3 If the Normans killed 75 rich soldiers, how many pieces of equipment could they take from them?

Harold and Alfred

4 If 635 poor soldiers and 128 rich soldiers threw their spears at the enemy, how many spears would fly through the air?

5 If 345 soldiers ran into battle and 128 were instantly killed by enemy arrows, how many would be left?

CHECK IT YOURSELF ✓

Your answer to 1 ⟶ ☐☐

Your answer to 2 ⟶ ☐☐

Your answer to 3 ⟶ ☐☐☐

Your answer to 4 ⟶ ☐☐☐

Your answer to 5 ⟶ ☐☐☐

Add them   Result ⟶ ☐☐☐☐

Do you get **1455**? *If not, check your answers and try again.*

Revolting Arithmetic: Invaders

Fierce Fighters

1 Anglo-Saxon soldiers had to provide their own equipment for battle. Poor men, like Harold, could only afford two pieces of equipment: a spear and a simple shield. Richer men, like Alfred, could afford five pieces of equipment: a decorated shield, cloak, brooch, spear and metal helmet. If each piece of equipment cost 1.5 pieces of silver, how many pieces of silver did it cost to equip a squad of four poor soldiers and two rich soldiers?

2 If the Danish invaders killed 367 poor soldiers, how many pieces of equipment could they take from them?

3 If the Normans killed 275 rich soldiers, how many pieces of equipment could they take from them?

4 If 2635 poor soldiers and 1428 rich soldiers threw their spears at the enemy, how many spears would fly through the air?

5 If 3645 soldiers ran into battle and 1128 were instantly killed by enemy arrows, how many would be left?

Harold and Alfred

CHECK IT YOURSELF ✔

Your answer to 1 ⟶ ▢ ▢

Your answer to 2 ⟶ ▢ ▢ ▢

Your answer to 3 ⟶ ▢ ▢ ▢ ▢

Add them   Result ⟶ ▢ ▢ ▢ ▢

Do you get **2136**? *If not, check your answers and try again.*

Your answer to 4 ⟶ ▢ ▢ ▢ ▢

Your answer to 5 ⟶ ▢ ▢ ▢ ▢

Add them   Result ⟶ ▢ ▢ ▢ ▢

Do you get **6580**? *If not, check your answers and try again.*

Village Values

1 Here is a map of an Anglo-Saxon village where Egbert, Hilda, Lief and Gilbert each own some land. Each strip of land is one acre. How many acres does Egbert have?

2 How many acres do the peasants of two villages this size have in total?

3 How many times more land does Lief have than Gilbert?

4 If Hilda and Egbert get married, how many acres of land do they have?

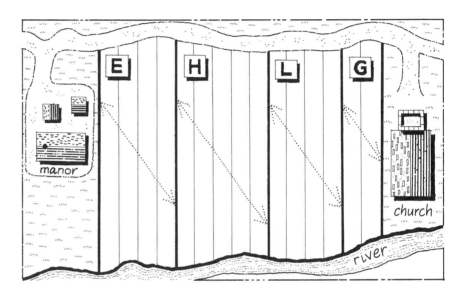

Key: E: Egbert H: Hilda L: Lief G: Gilbert

5 The biggest peasant landowner doubles the land she owns. How many acres does she now have?

CHECK IT YOURSELF ✔

Your answer to 1 ⟶ ☐

Your answer to 2 ⟶ ☐ ☐

Your answer to 3 ⟶ ☐

Your answer to 4 ⟶ ☐

Your answer to 5 ⟶ ☐ ☐

Add them   Result ⟶ ☐ ☐

Do you get **55**?
If not, check your answers and try again.

Revolting Arithmetic: *Invaders*

Village Values

1 Here is a map of an Anglo-Saxon village where Egbert, Hilda, Lief and Gilbert each own some land. Each strip of land is five acres. How many acres does Egbert have?

2 How many acres do the village peasants have in total?

3 How many times more land does Lief have than Gilbert?

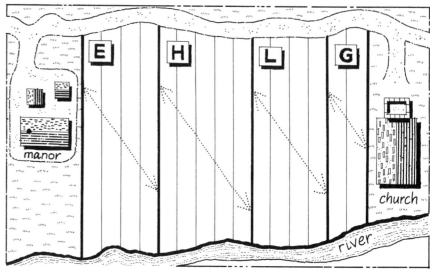

Key: E: Egbert   H: Hilda   L: Lief   G: Gilbert

4 If Hilda and Egbert get married, how many acres of land do they now own?

5 The biggest peasant landowner doubles the land that she owns. How many acres does she now have?

CHECK IT YOURSELF ✔

Your answer to 1 ⟶ ☐ ☐

Your answer to 2 ⟶ ☐ ☐

Your answer to 3 ⟶ ☐

Your answer to 4 ⟶ ☐ ☐

Your answer to 5 ⟶ ☐ ☐

Add them   Result ⟶ ☐ ☐ ☐

*Do you get **192**? If not, check your answers and try again.*

Revolting Arithmetic: *Invaders*

Village Values

1 Here is a map of an Anglo-Saxon village where Egbert, Hilda, Lief and Gilbert each own some land. Each strip of land is 2.5 acres. How many acres does Egbert have?

2 How many more acres does Egbert have than Gilbert?

3 If Hilda and Egbert get married, how many acres of land do they now own?

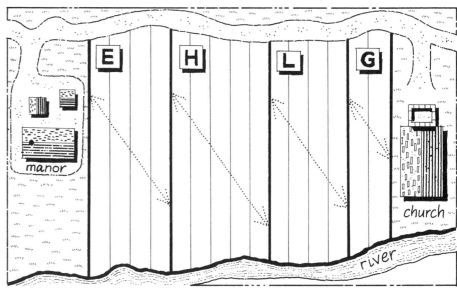

Key   E: Egbert   H: Hilda   L: Lief   G: Gilbert

4 Lief inherits Gilbert's land. How many acres does he then own?

5 The biggest peasant landowner doubles the land that she owns. How many acres does she now have?

CHECK IT YOURSELF ✔

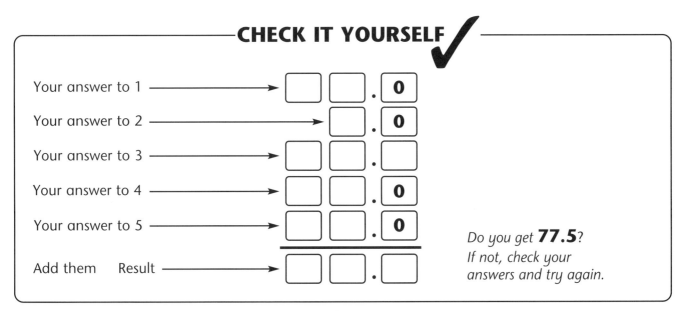

Your answer to 1 ⟶ ☐ ☐ . **0**

Your answer to 2 ⟶ ☐ . **0**

Your answer to 3 ⟶ ☐ ☐ . ☐

Your answer to 4 ⟶ ☐ ☐ . **0**

Your answer to 5 ⟶ ☐ ☐ . **0**

Add them   Result ⟶ ☐ ☐ . ☐

*Do you get **77.5**? If not, check your answers and try again.*

Raiderithmetic

1 Here is a map of the invasions that followed when the Roman armies left Britain in AD410. How many kilometres did the Vikings journey to Ireland?

2 How many different peoples settled in Britain and Ireland after the Roman armies left?

3 How much further than the Jutes did the Saxons have to sail to Britain?

4 Some Jutes lived nearer to Britain than others. If they were 50 kilometres nearer, how many kilometres did they have to sail?

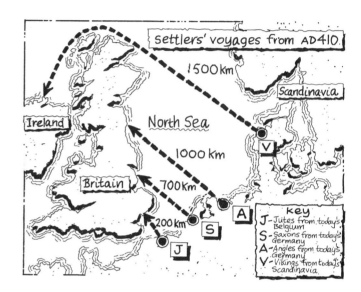

settlers' voyages from AD410.

1500 km

Scandinavia

Ireland

North Sea

1000 km

Britain

700 km

200 km

V

A

S

J

Key
J – Jutes from today's Belgium
S – Saxons from today's Germany
A – Angles from today's Germany
V – Vikings from today's Scandinavia

5 Some Saxons lived nearer to Britain than others. How many kilometres was the voyage for those who lived 80 kilometres nearer?

CHECK IT YOURSELF ✔

Your answer to 1 → ☐ ☐ ☐ ☐

Your answer to 2 ⟶ ☐

Your answer to 3 ⟶ ☐ ☐ ☐

Add them Result → **2** ☐ ☐ ☐

*Do you get **2004**?*
If not, check your answers and try again.

Your answer to 4 ⟶ ☐ ☐ ☐

Your answer to 5 ⟶ ☐ ☐ ☐

Add them Result ⟶ ☐ ☐ ☐

*Do you get **770**?*
If not, check your answers and try again.

Revolting Arithmetic: *Invaders*

Raiderithmetic

Here is a map of the invasions that followed when the Roman armies left Britain in AD410.

1 For Viking sailors, the Scottish coast was half-way to Ireland. How many kilometres was it to the Scottish coast?

2 How many kilometres was a return voyage to Britain for the Angles?

3 How many fewer kilometres did Jutes have to sail to Britain than Saxons?

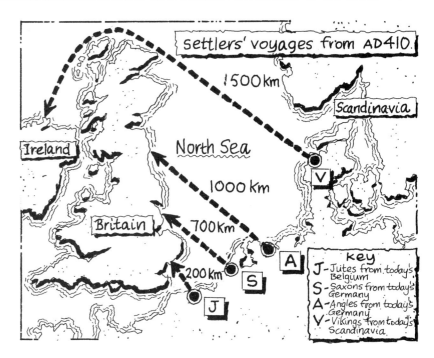

settlers' voyages from AD410.

1500 km

Scandinavia

North Sea

Ireland

1000 km

Britain

700 km

200 km

Key
J – Jutes from today's Belgium
S – Saxons from today's Germany
A – Angles from today's Germany
V – Vikings from today's Scandinavia

4 How many fewer kilometres did the Saxons sail to England than the Vikings on their journey to Ireland?

5 If 90 Vikings set out for Ireland and one-third were drowned on the way, how many arrived?

CHECK IT YOURSELF ✓

Your answer to 1 ⟶ ☐ ☐ ☐

Your answer to 2 ⟶ ☐ ☐ ☐ ☐

Your answer to 3 ⟶ ☐ ☐ ☐

Your answer to 4 ⟶ ☐ ☐ ☐

Your answer to 5 ⟶ ☐ ☐

Add them   Result ⟶ **4** ☐ ☐ ☐

*Do you get **4110**? If not, check your answers and try again.*

Raiderithmetic

Here is a map of the invasions that followed when the Roman armies left Britain in AD410.

1 How many kilometres was a return trip to Ireland for Viking sailors?

2 An Angle ship sank three-quarters of the way to Britain. How many kilometres from the British coast was it?

3 A Saxon longship made five return journeys between home and Britain. How many kilometres was that altogether?

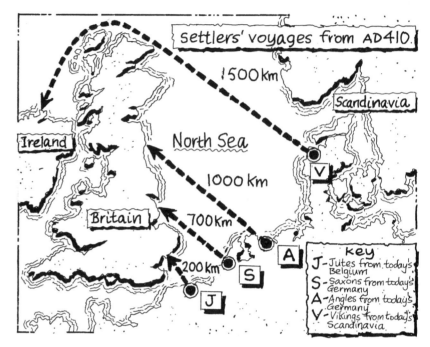

settlers' voyages from AD410.

1500 km

Scandinavia

North Sea

Ireland

1000 km

700 km

Britain

200 km

S

A

J

V

Key
J - Jutes from today's Belgium
S - Saxons from today's Germany
A - Angles from today's Germany
V - Vikings from today's Scandinavia

4 A fleet of 35 Viking longships set out for Ireland. Each held 55 settlers. How many settlers were aboard the fleet?

5 If 960 Vikings set out for Ireland in 15 longships and one-sixth were drowned on the way, how many got there?

CHECK IT YOURSELF ✔

Your answer to 1 ⟶ ☐ ☐ ☐ ☐

Your answer to 2 ⟶ ☐ ☐ ☐

Your answer to 3 ⟶ ☐ ☐ ☐ ☐

Your answer to 4 ⟶ ☐ ☐ ☐ ☐

Your answer to 5 ⟶ ☐ ☐ ☐

Add them   Result ⟶ ☐ ☐ ☐ ☐ ☐

Do you get **12 975**?
If not, check your answers and try again.

Feasting Fun

Historians found a list of goods required for a feast for the King of Wessex:

10 geese	300 loaves	10 cheeses
2 oxen	10 jars of honey	5 salmon
42 casks of ale	20 chickens	20 pounds of hay

1 How many birds are there?

2 How many ox legs are there?

3 Suppose each cheese were cut into eight pieces. How many pieces would there be?

4 If each salmon were cut in half, how many pieces would there be?

5 If the king ordered the supply of ale to be doubled, how many casks would be required?

CHECK IT YOURSELF ✔

Your answer to 1 ⟶ ☐ ☐

Your answer to 2 ⟶ ☐

Your answer to 3 ⟶ ☐ ☐

Your answer to 4 ⟶ ☐ ☐

Your answer to 5 ⟶ ☐ ☐

Add them   Result ⟶ ☐ ☐ ☐

Do you get **212**? *If not, check your answers and try again.*

Feasting Fun

Historians found a list of goods required for a feast for the King of Wessex. You can see that it was not a vegetarian meal!

10 geese	300 loaves	10 cheeses
2 oxen	10 jars of honey	5 salmon
42 casks of ale	20 chickens	20 pounds of hay

1 If all the birds were cut into six pieces, how many servings of bird would there be?

2 If the ox legs were cut into 14 pieces, how many servings of ox leg would there be?

3 Suppose two large cheeses were each divided into 108 pieces. How many servings would there be?

4 If each salmon were cut into 24 pieces, how many servings would there be?

5 If two casks of ale served nine people, how many people would 42 casks serve?

CHECK IT YOURSELF ✔

Your answer to 1 ⟶ ▢ ▢ ▢

Your answer to 2 ⟶ ▢ ▢ ▢

Your answer to 3 ⟶ ▢ ▢ ▢

Your answer to 4 ⟶ ▢ ▢ ▢

Your answer to 5 ⟶ ▢ ▢ ▢

Add them   Result ⟶ ▢ ▢ ▢

Do you get **817**?
If not, check your answers and try again.

Feasting Fun

Historians found a list of goods required for a feast for the King of Wessex. You can see that it was not a vegetarian meal!

10 geese	300 loaves	10 cheeses
2 oxen	10 jars of honey	5 salmon
42 casks of ale	20 chickens	20 pounds of hay

1 If the hay were given to eight horses, how many ounces would each receive? (There are 16 ounces in a pound.)

2 If the ox legs were cut into 123 pieces, how many servings of ox leg would there be?

3 One of the cheeses is shared by a table of eight guests. What percentage of the cheese can each person have?

4 If each salmon weighed eight and a half ounces, how many ounces would there be altogether?

5 If the king ordered each cask of ale to be divided into 56 portions, how many servings of ale would there be?

CHECK IT YOURSELF ✔

Your answer to 1 ──────→ ☐ ☐ . **0**

Your answer to 2 ─────→ ☐ ☐ ☐ . **0**

Your answer to 3 ─────→ ☐ ☐ . ☐

Your answer to 4 ─────→ ☐ ☐ . ☐

Your answer to 5 ──→ ☐ ☐ ☐ ☐ . **0**

Add them   Result ──→ ☐ ☐ ☐ ☐ . ☐

*Do you get **3431.0**? If not, check your answers and try again.*

Longship Logic

1 This is a picture of a Viking longship, built to voyage all over the world. The oarsmen hung their shields on either side of the longship. Count the shields. How many oarsmen are there on this side?

2 A Viking longship could easily voyage a thousand kilometres. Write that number in figures.

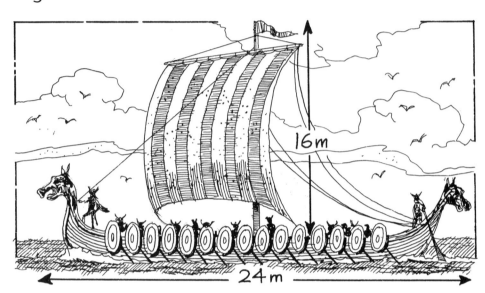

16m

24m

3 How many metres long is the longship?

4 By how many metres is the boat longer than its mast?

5 If two longboats sail one behind the other, with five metres between them, how many metres long are they altogether?

CHECK IT YOURSELF ✓

Your answer to 1 ——————→ ☐ ☐

Your answer to 2 —→ ☐ ☐ ☐ ☐

Your answer to 3 ——————→ ☐ ☐

Your answer to 4 ————————→ ☐

Your answer to 5 ——————→ ☐ ☐

Add them Result —→ **1** ☐ ☐ ☐

Do you get **1100**? *If not, check your answers and try again.*

Revolting Arithmetic: *Invaders*

Longship Logic

1 This is a picture of a Viking longship, built to voyage all over the world. The oarsmen hung their shields on either side of the longship. Count the shields. How many oarsmen are on the ship altogether?

2 Viking longships are believed to have voyaged over ten thousand kilometres. Write that number in figures.

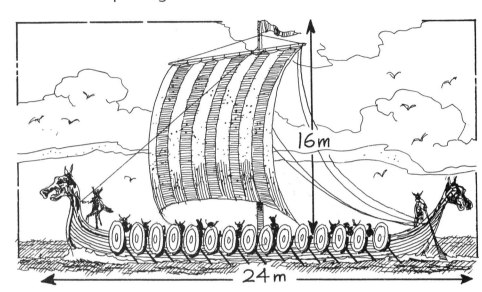

3 Five longboats are moored nose-to-tail. How many metres long are they altogether?

4 By how many metres is the boat longer than its mast?

5 A Viking sailor typically stood two metres tall. The longship's mast is the height of how many sailors?

CHECK IT YOURSELF ✓

Your answer to 1 ⟶ ☐ ☐

Your answer to 2 ⟶ ☐ ☐ ☐ ☐ ☐

Your answer to 3 ⟶ ☐ ☐ ☐

Your answer to 4 ⟶ ☐

Your answer to 5 ⟶ ☐

Add them   Result ⟶ **1** **0** ☐ ☐ ☐

*Do you get **10 166**? If not, check your answers and try again.*

Longship Logic

1 This is a picture of a Viking longship, built to voyage all over the world. The oarsmen hung their shields on either side of the longship. Count the shields. How many oarsmen are there altogether on a fleet of five ships?

2 Viking longships are believed to have voyaged 6700 kilometres to North America from Sweden. How far is that to the nearest 1000 kilometres?

3 Twenty-five longboats are moored nose-to-tail with one metre between each pair. How many metres do they occupy altogether?

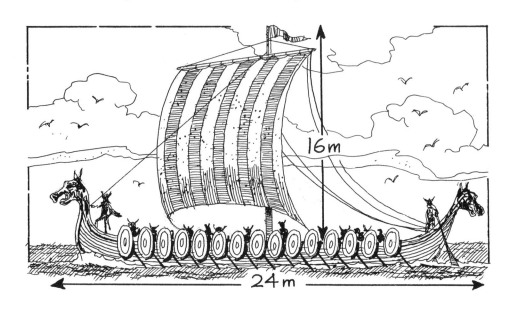

4 A Viking captain wanted a ship that was 50 per cent bigger than this one.
a) How many metres long would it be?
b) How many metres high would the mast be?

CHECK IT YOURSELF ✔

Your answer to 1 ⟶ ☐☐☐

Your answer to 2 ⟶ ☐☐☐☐

Your answer to 3 ⟶ ☐☐☐

Your answer to 4a ⟶ ☐☐

Your answer to 4b ⟶ ☐☐

Add them   Result ⟶ ☐☐☐☐

*Do you get **7834**? If not, check your answers and try again.*

Abbess Addings

1. Abbess Hilda became a nun at the age of 33 in the year AD six hundred and forty-seven. Write that year in figures.

2. Ten years later she founded her own monastery at Whitby. In what year did she found the monastery?

3. The King of Northumbria held a conference at Hilda's monastery seven years after she had founded it. In what year was that?

4. Hilda's monastery became very famous and one-tenth of her 50 monks became bishops. How many is that?

5. The people loved Hilda. After she died, in AD680, aged 66, the Church made her a saint. In what year was she born?

CHECK IT YOURSELF ✔

Your answer to 1 ⟶ ▢ ▢ ▢

Your answer to 2 ⟶ ▢ ▢ ▢

Add them   Result ⟶ **1** **3** ▢ ▢

Do you get **1304**? *If not, check your answers and try again.*

Your answer to 3 ⟶ ▢ ▢ ▢

Your answer to 4 ⟶ ▢

Your answer to 5 ⟶ ▢ ▢ ▢

Add them   Result ⟶ **1** **2** ▢ ▢

Do you get **1283**? *If not, check your answers and try again.*

Abbess Addings

1 Abbess Hilda was a member of the royal family of Northumbria. She became a nun at the age of 33 in the year AD647. In what year was she born?

2 Ten years later she founded her own monastery at Whitby and taught the people of Northumbria how to say their prayers. If she said two prayers for each of her 30 prayer beads, how many prayers would she say?

3 The invaders of Britain respected Hilda's views. The King of Northumbria held a conference at her monastery. If there were 153 nuns and monks already at the monastery (including Hilda), and 128 people attended the conference, how many were there altogether?

4 Hilda was independent and outspoken. Her monastery became very famous and one in every ten of her 50 monks became bishops. How many is that?

5 The people loved Hilda. They called her 'the mother'. After she died, at the age of 66, the Church made her a saint. In what year did she die?

CHECK IT YOURSELF ✔

Your answer to 1 ⟶ ☐ ☐ ☐

Your answer to 2 ⟶ ☐ ☐

Your answer to 3 ⟶ ☐ ☐ ☐

Your answer to 4 ⟶ ☐

Your answer to 5 ⟶ ☐ ☐ ☐

Add them   Result ⟶ ☐ ☐ ☐ ☐

Do you get **1640**? *If not, check your answers and try again.*

Abbess Addings

1 Abbess Hilda was a member of the royal family of Northumbria. She was baptised alongside the king, 156 months after her birth in the year AD614. How old was she?

2 At the age of 43, she founded her own monastery at Whitby and taught the people of Northumbria how to say their prayers. If she said 12 prayers for each of her 30 prayer beads, how many prayers would she say?

3 The invaders of Britain respected Hilda's views. The King of Northumbria held a conference at her monastery seven years after she founded it. If there were 153 nuns and monks at the monastery (including Hilda), and twice as many people travelled to the conference, how many were there altogether?

4 Hilda was independent and outspoken. Her monastery became very famous and ten per cent of her 50 monks became bishops. How many is that?

5 The people loved Hilda. After she died, aged 66, the Church made her a saint. If there were nine monks when she built Whitby Abbey and almost 7.5 times as many when she died, how many were there at her death?

CHECK IT YOURSELF ✔

Your answer to 1 ⟶ ☐ ☐

Your answer to 2 ⟶ ☐ ☐ ☐

Your answer to 3 ⟶ ☐ ☐ ☐

Your answer to 4 ⟶ ☐

Your answer to 5 ⟶ ☐ ☐

Add them   Result ⟶ ☐ ☐ ☐

*Do you get **904**? If not, check your answers and try again.*

Answers

British Battles

Level 1
1. $43 + 54 = 97$
2. $61 - 43 = 18$
3. $2 \times 2 = 4$
4. $\frac{1}{2}$

Level 2
1. $43 + 54 = 97 = 100 = 1$
2. $75 \times 9 = 675$
3. $8 \times 3 = 24 + 1 = 25$
4. 1 man + 1 man + 1 woman $= \frac{1}{3}$

Level 3
1. $97 - 54 = $ AD43
2. $60\,000 - 42\,867 = 17\,133$
3. $950 \times 3 = 2850 + 12\,500 = 15\,350$
4. $25\,000 \times 2 = 50\,000$

Roman Roads

Level 1
1. 3
2. 110
3. $110 + 85 = 195$
4. $85 + 120 = 205$
5. $85 + 85 = 170$

Level 2
1. $120 + 85 + 100 = 305$
2. $140 + 120 = 260$
3. $85 + 110 = 195 + 195 = 390$
4. $100 + 85 + 140 = 325$
5. $120 \div 3 = 40$

Level 3
1. $(100 + 200 = 300) + (140 + 120 = 260)$
   $+ (110 + 85 = 195)$
   $= 300 + 260 + 195 = 755$
2. $140 + 85 + 100 + 100 + 200 = 625$
3. $140 + 120 = 260 \div 2 = 130$
   $140 - 130 = 10$
4. $140 \div 10 = 14$
5. $140 + 110 = 250 \div 8 = 31.25 = 31$

Slave Statistics

Level 1
1. 73
2. $132 - 73 = 59$
3. $5 \times 8 = 40$
4. $12 \div 2 = 6$

Level 2
1. $60\,000$
2. $21 \div 3 = 7$
   $21 - 7 = 14$
3. $15 \times 8 = 120$
4. $15 \div 5 = 3$
   $15 - 3 = 12$

Level 3
1. $42\,550 + 17\,450 = 60\,000$
2. $20\,000 \times 4 = 80\,000$
3. $8.4 \times 9 = 75.6 = 76$
4. $12 \times \frac{75}{100} = 9$
   $12 - 9 = 3$

Answers

Ghastly Gladiators

Level 1
1. 250
2. 2 + 3 + 2 = 7
3. 121 − 36 = 85
4. 8 x 2 = 16

Level 2
1. 10 000
2. 2 + 3 + 2 = 7
   5 x 7 = 35
3. 245 − 186 = 59
4. 14 x 2 = 28

Level 3
1. $2\frac{1}{2}$ x 2 = 5 x 3 = 15 x 4 = 60
2. 2 + 3 + 2 = 7
   32 x 7 = 224
3. 25% = $\frac{1}{4}$ x 2440 = 610
   2440 − 610 = 1830
4. 54 x 2 = 108 ÷ 3 = 36
   108 − 36 = 72

Kingdoms & Counties

Level 1
1. 38
2. 29 + 17 = 46
3. 6 + 5 + 4 + 5 = 20
4. 38 + 29 = 67 − 14 = 53

Level 2
1. 17 + 29 + 38 + 6 + 5 + 4 + 5
   = 104
2. 29 + 17 = 46 x 9 = 414
3. 6 + 5 + 4 + 5 = 20 x 7 = 140
4. 29 + 38 = 67 x 8 = 536

Level 3
1. 17 + 29 + 38 + 6 + 5 + 4 + 5
   = 104 x 9 = 936
2. 29 + 17 = 46 x 36 = 1656
3. 6 + 5 + 4 + 5 = 20 x 55 = 1100
4. 29 + 38 = 67 x 28 = 1876

Farming Figures

Level 1
1. 142
2. 58 + 33 = 91
3. 12 + 12 + 12 = 36
4. 15 + 1 + 12 = 28
5. 5 + 1 + 18 = 24

Level 2
1. 72 x $\frac{1}{2}$ = 72 ÷ 2 = 36
2. 12 x 9 = 108
3. 15 ÷ 3 = 5 x 5 = 25
   5 x 2 = 10 x 6 = 60 + 25 = 85
4. 5 x 12 = 60 x $\frac{1}{2}$ = 60 ÷ 2 = 30

Level 3
1. 1 + 14 = 15 x 72 = 1080
2. 9 x 12 = 108 x 12 = 1296
3. 16 x 25% = 16 ÷ 4 = 4 x 5 = 20
   16 x 75% = (16 x 3) ÷ 4 = 12 x 3
   = 36 + 20 = 56
4. 14 x 12 = 168 x $\frac{1}{2}$ = 168 ÷ 2 = 84

Answers

Nave, Tower & Transept

Level 1
1 650
2 20
3 40
4 10
5 5 + 12 = 17

Level 2
1 90
2 12 x 8 = 96
3 5 x 5 = 25 + 96 = 121
4 121 + 12 + 24 = 157
5 9 x 12 = 108

Level 3
1 180
2 21 x 14 = 294
3 12 x 12 = 144 + 294 = 438
4 438 ÷ 10 = 43.8 + 438 = 481.8
5 11 x 21 = 231

Fierce Fighters

Level 1
1 Harold: 2
   Alfred: 5 + 2 = 7
2 9 x 2 = 18
3 8 x 5 = 40
4 135 + 28 = 163
5 345 − 28 = 317

Level 2
1 2 x 8 = 16
   5 x 2 = 10 + 16 = 26
2 37 x 2 = 74
3 75 x 5 = 375
4 635 + 128 = 763
5 345 − 128 = 217

Level 3
1 2 x 4 = 8 x 1.5 = 12
   5 x 2 = 10 x 1.5 = 15 + 12 = 27
2 367 x 2 = 734
3 275 x 5 = 1375
4 2635 + 1428 = 4063
5 3645 − 1128 = 2517

Village Values

Level 1
1 4 x 1 = 4
2 4 + 5 + 4 + 2 = 15 x 2 = 30
3 4 ÷ 2 = 2
4 4 + 5 = 9
5 5 x 2 = 10

Level 2
1 4 x 5 = 20
2 (4 x 5) + (5 x 5) + (4 x 5) + (2 x 5)
   = 20 + 25 + 20 + 10 = 75
3 20 ÷ 10 = 2
4 20 + 25 = 45
5 2 x 25 = 50

Level 3
1 4 x 2.5 = 10
2 (4 x 2.5 = 10) − (2 x 2.5 = 5)
   = 10 − 5 = 5
3 (4 x 2.5 = 10) + (5 x 2.5 = 12.5)
   = 10 + 12.5 = 22.5
4 (4 x 2.5 = 10) + (2 x 2.5 = 5)
   = 10 + 5 = 15
5 2 x 5 = 10 x 2.5 = 25

Answers

Raiderithmetic

Level 1
1. 1500
2. 4
3. 700 − 200 = 500
4. 200 − 50 = 150
5. 700 − 80 = 620

Level 2
1. 1500 ÷ 2 = 750
2. 1000 + 1000 = 2000
3. 700 − 200 = 500
4. 1500 − 700 = 800
5. 90 ÷ 3 = 30
   90 − 30 = 60

Level 3
1. 1500 + 1500 = 3000
2. $1000 \times \frac{3}{4} = 750$
   1000 − 750 = 250
3. 700 x 2 = 1400 x 5 = 7000
4. 35 x 55 = 1925
5. 960 − (960 ÷ 6 = 160) = 800

Feasting Fun

Level 1
1. 10 + 20 = 30
2. 2 x 4 = 8
3. 8 x 10 = 80
4. 5 x 2 = 10
5. 42 x 2 = 84

Level 2
1. 10 + 20 = 30 x 6 = 180
2. 2 x 4 = 8 x 14 = 112
3. 108 + 108 = 216
4. 5 x 24 = 120
5. 42 ÷ 2 = 21 x 9 = 189

Level 3
1. 20 x 16 = 320 ÷ 8 = 40
2. 2 x 4 = 8 x 123 = 984
3. $\frac{1}{8} = \frac{12.5}{100} = 12.5\%$
4. 5 x 8.5 = 42.5
5. 42 x 56 = 2352

Longship Logic

Level 1
1. 15
2. 1000
3. 24
4. 24 − 16 = 8
5. 24 + 5 + 24 = 53

Level 2
1. 15 x 2 = 30
2. 10 000
3. 24 x 5 = 120
4. 24 − 16 = 8
5. 16 ÷ 2 = 8

Level 3
1. 15 x 2 = 30 x 5 = 150
2. 7000
3. 24 x 25 = 600 + 24 = 624
4a. $24 \times \frac{50}{100} = 12$
   24 + 12 = 36
4b. $16 \times \frac{50}{100} = 8$
   16 + 8 = 24

Revolting Arithmetic: *Invaders*

Answers

Abbess Addings

Level 1
1. 647
2. 647 + 10 = 657
3. 657 + 7 = 664
4. $50 \times \frac{1}{10} = 50 \div 10 = 5$
5. 680 − 66 = 614

Level 2
1. 647 − 33 = 614
2. 30 × 2 = 60
3. 128 + 153 = 281
4. $50 \times \frac{1}{10} = 50 \div 10 = 5$
5. 614 + 66 = 680

Level 3
1. 156 ÷ 12 = 13
2. 30 × 12 = 360
3. 153 + (2 × 153 = 306) = 153 + 306 = 459
4. 50 × 10% = 500 ÷ 100 = 5
5. 9 × 7.5 = 67.5 = 67